Don,

Wishing you many
happy Voyages through
life

Dawn + Rob Oldenburger

P.O. Box 441
MORNINGTON.
VIC. AUST.

DINGO KING

DINGO

KING

Ivan Smith

With paintings and drawings by
Clifton Pugh

 wren

WREN PUBLISHING PTY LTD
2 Palmer Street, South Melbourne

© Text: Ivan Smith 1977
© Paintings and line drawings: Clifton Pugh 1977

First Published 1977
Set by Trade Composition Pty Ltd, Melbourne
Printed and bound by Toppan, Hong Kong
Designed by Derrick I. Stone

National Library of Australia C-I-P data

Smith, Ivan
  Dingo King

  ISBN 0 85885 209 8.

  I. Pugh, Clifton Ernest, 1924-, illus.
  II. Title

A823.3

Foreword
Sir Peter Scott

THE NEW GROUNDS
SLIMBRIDGE
GLOUCESTER
GL2 7BT

Dingoes are part of the web — the ecological web of interdependence which orders all life in the Australian outback — the plants and the animals, the predator and the prey.

For seven human generations, dingoes have had the sheep farmer as their implacable enemy. Yet they have managed to hang on into a new age of human enlightenment where the value of the predator to the total ecosystem is coming to be understood.

Ivan Smith has brilliantly captured the interdependence in his urgent, almost explosive prose . . . and Clifton Pugh has, no less brilliantly, captured the visual images of the Australian wilderness.

I am honoured and delighted to be allowed to contribute a foreword to a distinguished book by two very distinguished Australians.

Peter Scott.

Author's Introduction:

The text of this book was originally conceived several years ago, as one of a trilogy of interlocking radio feature broadcasts. Each programme looked at the same set of human situations from a different viewpoint, and animals were used as symbols to synthesize certain groups of human attributes.

The three vantage-points were those of the dingo, of the wombat, and of the kangaroo. What they represented overlapped, and conflicted. I was wanting to write about the opposition of toughness and tenderness in human life, and to analyze success and failure. The wombat came at the tender end of the scale, the dingo at the tough end. It seemed to me that both qualities, in differing contexts of life, could be admired, and that both could be regarded with misgiving and suspicion. And it still seems to me that, somehow, like all aspects of behaviour, they have to be reconciled in any comprehension of humanity.

In thinking about all this, I found that I was often contradicting myself, and confusing myself; and so I tried to separate conflicting viewpoints into programmes that could be taken individually, and also contrasted.

In *The Death of a Wombat* the focus was on failure, and on the dubious nature of innocence and tenderness. In *Dingo King* the emphasis was on ruthlessness and the debatable values of success. When is toughness admirable? When is it despicable? Can the end *always* justify the means? To what extent is ruthlessness necessary to achieve satisfying working and private lives?

I haven't found any easy answers. There are so many avenues of thought to follow, and so few conclusions to come to.

As a result, both *The Death of a Wombat* and *Dingo King* are allegories — starting points for speculation.

There is only one thing that these companions of the Australian bush share with each other and with all the plant and animal life of this planet — with all the powerful and feeble methods they may command, they must urgently try to survive.

Artist's Introduction:

This is the second book of a trilogy. The first, *The Death of a Wombat*, showed the effect of fire upon the landscape, with the wombat as the central character.

Dingo King shows just what drought does to people, animals and the land. The third, yet to come, will be the result of flood and the central character will be a kangaroo.

I hope that this book, *Dingo King*, awakes some awareness in people of the very delicate balance in nature, the tenuous thread reaching through us to plants, animals and the very soil. Experience has shown us that if we destroy one part, we throw the rest out of balance.

We have reached a dangerous state now in this country and I think Ivan Smith has caught that sense of urgency in the tempo of his prose. I feel honoured to work again in collaboration with him and hope, with my paintings, I can express love, hope and fear for this land, remembering we are only its guardians.

Problems of the environment are not particular to Australia. When Sir Peter Scott agreed to write a foreword to this book, it was important to me not only because of the respect I have for him and his achievements, but also because he is a world figure in conservation. In the United Kingdom, his own country, through his paintings and through the Wild-fowl Trusts, Sir Peter has focused public attention on the plight of birds and the environment. Through his world-wide work, particularly through the World Wildlife Fund, he has emphasised the need for countries and people everywhere to co-operate to preserve the balance of nature.

The sun is a silver disc
at the centre of a set of wide, blue rings.

Gum-leaves have curled and blackboy-leaves
have hardened as the rise of sap has slowed
in trunks and branches.

Earthworms shift deeper for moist soil.
Pin-points of light in the sand
have crumbled to brown powder.

MORNING OF THE DINGO
Oil on Canvas 122 × 157 cms (48 × 62 ins)

A ridge curves above a valley
where a two-pronged stream moves
more slowly week by week,
the tributaries dead,
the trails of water dying.
Some rivers are dead,
others have shrunk to strings of pools,
but there are many that stay.
There is still pale green in the field
shaped by the fork,
where the heavy-fleeced sheep
bunch and totter.
Their thin feet stumble on carcases,
some shorn, and others abandoned for meat or wool,
all of them left unburied to
distract predators
from the sheep still living.

THE BEGINNING OF THE DROUGHT
Gouache 56 × 76 cms (22 × 30 ins)

THE LAST WATER
Gouache 57 × 78 cms (22½ × 30¾ ins)

It would need remarkable eyesight
to discern the form of a dingo
in the blending shadows of the ridge.
He doesn't often move along high ground.
He usually keeps to lower paths in a valley,
but the drought is persistent,
and his mate of the last two years
has thrown pups in calm,
animal agony,
and so he has gone high to watch the sheep.

THE CARCASES
Gouache 50 × 71 cms (19¾ × 22 ins)

He has rarely attacked sheep
in his eight years,
but the drought has cancelled
birds and fish and bush-rats.

Lying in the shade,
paws scuffing the dust,
he has watched the sheep for hours.
He is hunter,
not scavenger,
and living animals give more moisture.
He moves higher,
and comes to the edge of the ridge's crest,
and looks at everything he can see.

Not a dog.
Not a wolf.
This is his country.
And he is king of it.

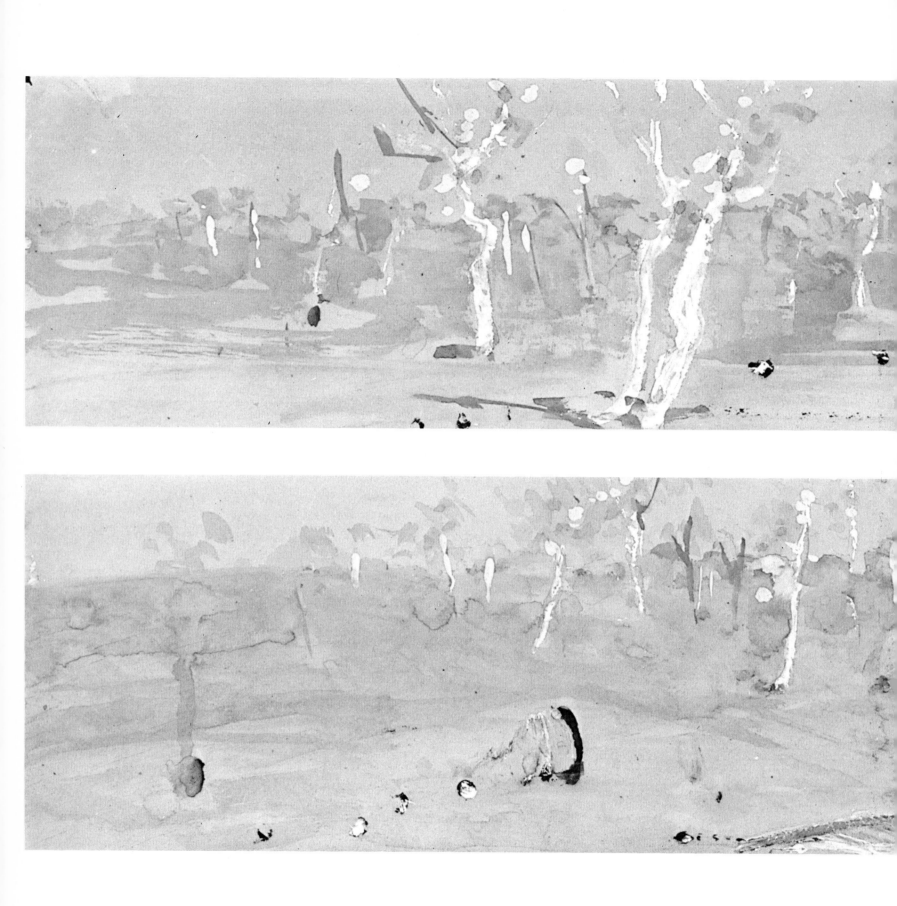

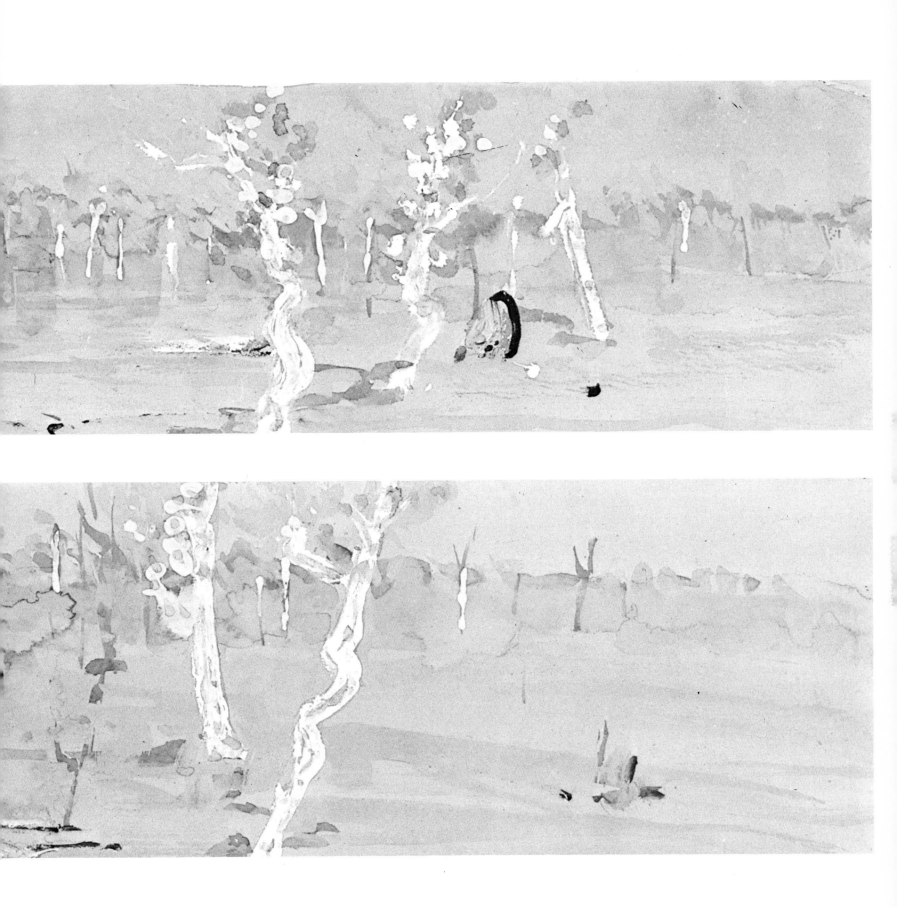

Bacteria race in the stems of hay,
and swell the nodules of wheat.
Mucus dries in the gut of sheep,
delaying flesh and fat.

The land burns
and the air stares.

THE KANGAROO WAR
Oil on Canvas 91 × 122 cms (36 × 48 ins)

The old mind of the dingo weighs up the old,
old dangers.
Death by thirst,
which he has seen;
death by kangaroo,
when a dingo was too tired to measure
the energy he had spent;
curious injury by wombat,
when a wombat suddenly crunches
a dingo's ribs against the roof of a burrow;
death by man,
the source of many scents
and of explosions in the earth.

In drought the dangers are dulled
in the eight-year-old mind.
Two pups,
a mate who normally heads the hunt for food
but who now must stay near the den,
scarcer meat
— the facts melt through his brain and frame.
Perhaps a dog,
perhaps a wolf.
The long, lean, broad-browed head tilts back,
the eyes close,
and the tongue loops past the wide-spaced teeth.
There are no men now,
though there *have* been men.
These are the first sheep for five days.
He begins to decide.

Drought produces a quiet that is unusual
even for the Australian bush.
Some birds reach the coast-line,
others are stilled.

THE STILLNESS OF SUMMER
Gouache 56 × 76 cms (22 × 30 ins)

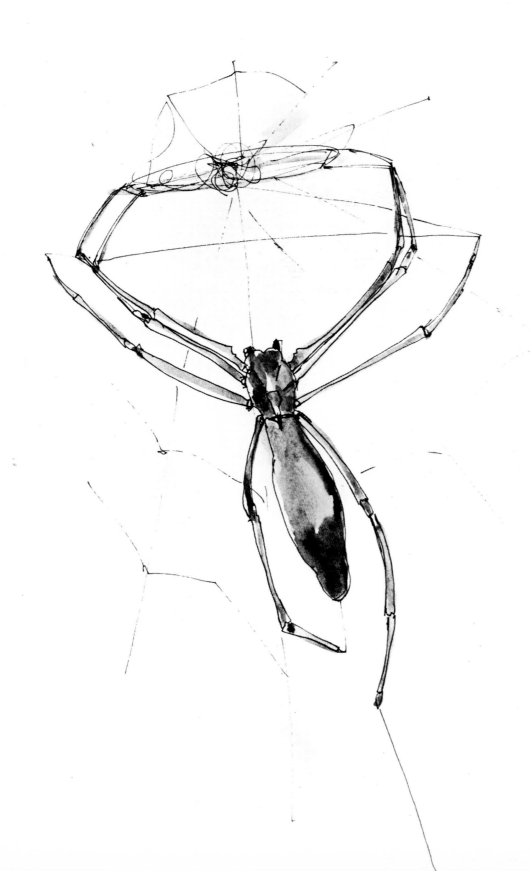

The chatter of rabbits lessens,
there is no shrilling of cicadas,
and koala-muttering in the eucalypts
fades in the first months of dryness.
But some sounds belong to drought.

The jeering of crows is harsher,
and bark splinters from trees with sharp snaps.

SNAPPING OF BEAKS AND BARK
Oil on Hardboard 91 × 122 cms (36 × 48 ins)

Kangaroos travel by day when the days are right,
but by night when the days are wrong,
and the search for water is urgent.
The thundering of kangaroo herds
after dark is a source of wonder,
and a warning.
Men know that kangaroos move in larger groups in drought,
and are much more easily trapped for their
hide and meat.

And they think that killing them
saves the grasslands for sheep.

THE RUN OF EMUS
Oil on Hardboard 91 × 122 cms (36 × 48 ins)

The rump of a wombat is pushed and shoved,
backward and upward,
out of a burrow.
He looks at the burrow's mouth.
Films of sand drift down the sides
and sift past stones on the floor.
The wombat sweeps the sand away,
using his nose as a spade.
Some slides back.
He rests to think.
The eyes in the flat,
spread head blink slowly;
the nose distorts and the brain wrinkles.
He has burrowed deep for the dampness
that holds up walls.
He decides this morning to fetch more stones.

The dingo slides down the half-lit
side of the ridge.
Not even the sharp-eared hare
would catch a sound of him,
and the kangaroo would move away
in deference to his sovereignty.
The dingo is the direct descendant
of the Asian Pale-foot wolf.
In the thousands of years he has lived in Australia
he has become a species of his own.
He has hardened and attuned his muscle
and mind to mastery.
The men of his country spend time
and millions of dollars
on traps and planes and trappers
and fences to dethrone a king.
It is called the dingo-war.

The back half of a wombat
weighs rather more than the front.
Short legs guide a fatty hump
in a slow, erratic walk.
He returns with a piece of rock in his mouth.
A cub comes out of the burrow.
The rock is dropped
and the wombat starts to play,
a matter of nudges and shoves
and of stumbling forward and back.
He plumps himself over the cub
(which is where it sometimes sleeps)
but the cub's squirming is weak.
The slitted eyes look across to the burrow.
Something is wrong.

45

The gold fur of the dingo mingles
and disentangles with the shadows of the scrub.
Body and head and tail sink lower as he glides,
slowing sometimes,
never stopping,
and nose and ears and paws tell him
the way to go.
He crosses a ford at the upper,
closer river-fork.
He swims easily and well.
The wombat swims with uncertain heaves
and is glad of the bank again.
The kangaroo edges forward
with painfully threshing legs.
The dingo leaves his body to his line of Asian sires,
which favoured the slimness and strength
of the grey-hound wolves,
and rejected the blood of the mastiff-wolves
that men bred for their size and anger.
The legs rudder the body to the bank
and he slides onto ground.

SCRUB
Oil on Hardboard 122×91 cms (48×36 ins)

47

Wheat-stems bend down
as bacteria soften the nodules.
Stalks of grass are laced with slits
and heat sears the inner cellulose.

Two hundred kilometres away,
wet air is drawn across the coast as warm,
dry inland air moves upward.

The dingo is motionless,
near the bank of the further river,
There is a long,
tight quivering of fore-legs,
and a sudden, silent,
vertical rush.
Neck arched down,
legs rigid,
he drops back to earth
and his jaws crunch on a bush-rat underneath layers of grass.
The little rodent concealed himself from sight
but not from hearing:
his slight rustling and the dingo's soundless pounce
have lead to an earlier death than thirst.
He was food for older marsupials before the dingo came;
the pouched wolf and the Tasmanian devil
were heavier and stronger,
but slower and less skilled,
and they now live only where the dingo has not yet gone.
The dingo survives by sight and hearing and smell;
he rules by speed and endurance,
and a sparing use and a frequent renewing of his deep energy.

The kangaroos have slept in a hunched mass,
in a littering of twitching necks
and tails.
One by one they wake
and subtract themselves from the huddle,
and lope in widening circles,
sampling food where they can.
Today they will decide whether to return to a place
that smelt of water,
or whether tonight they will take up again
their southward race with drought.
There is danger north,
and risks in the south,
and danger too
in the hardening of the leaves they tug from trees.

Be stiff!
Still!
Ears, tail, shoulders like stone!
A slow swaying back of the whole body,
beginning by adding tension to the muscles in the haunches,
a delicate rearing
till the front paw leaves the earth.
The dingo rests
to let his panting swell and slacken.
The rough skin of Australia has abraded the pads of his paws,
but the tips stay sensitive,
and have detected what nose and eyes did not
— a black,
pitted streak of sunken iron.

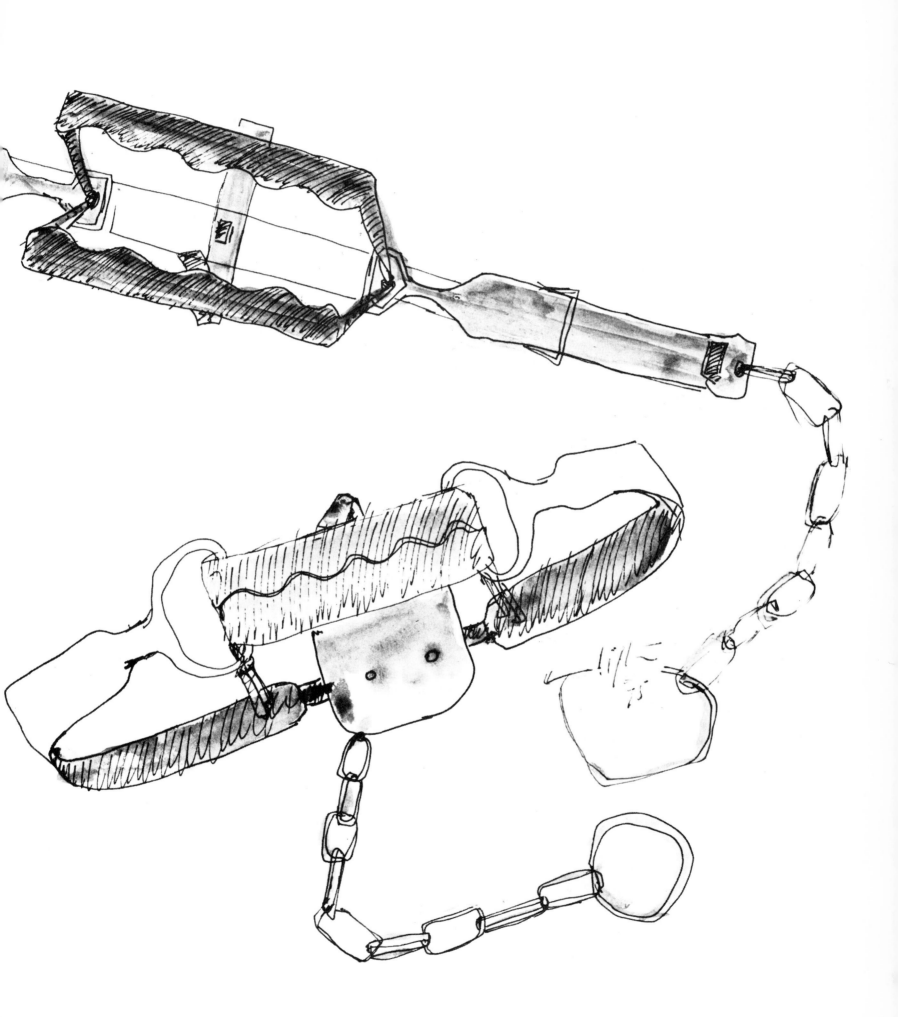

The dingo stands,
and spots the place with warning urine.
Once he saw a dingo caught in a trap.
It chewed off its paw to escape,
but could never hunt alone again.

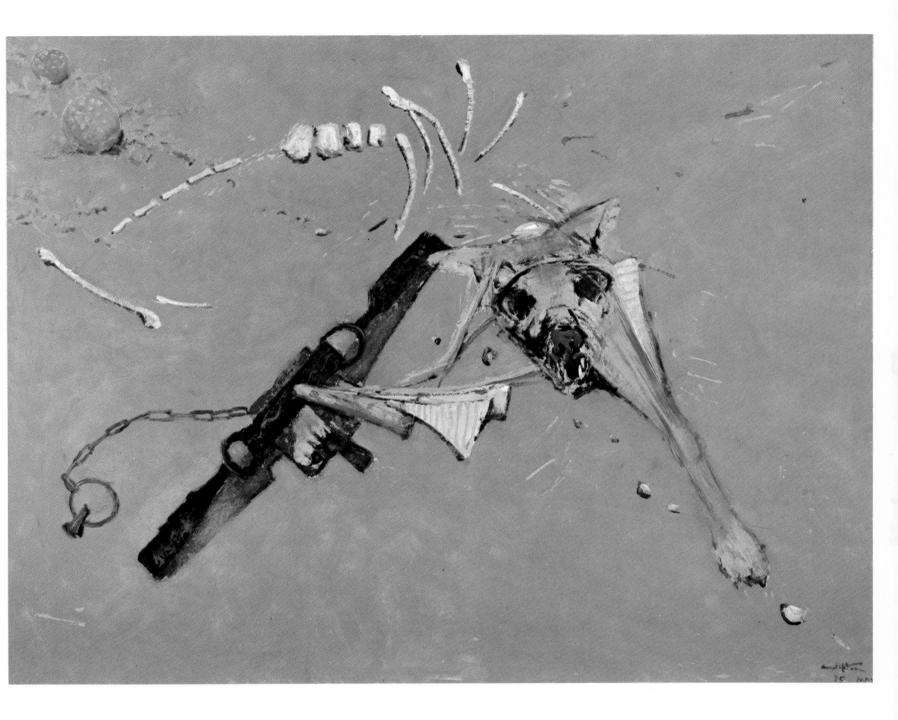

THE DINGO WAR
Oil on Hardboard 91 × 122 cms (36 × 48 ins)

The wombat lies on his side to dig.
The cub does nothing.
The scimitared claws droop,
and the wombat thinks.
He has sometimes gone to the river
for moisture and soaking leaves,
but he has never taken the cub.
The river can mean dead animals,
noise and fear.
He rolls upright,
and carefully levers the listless cub to its feet.
Using his nose as a prod,
with fore-paws stretched to either side,
he pushes the cub along with a patient shuffling.

Two hundred kilometres away,
three kilometres high,
the wet air–mass is folded back.
Rising masses of hot,
sharp air thrust it away from the land.

A succulent sticks from a rabbit's mouth;
ants stitch trails through its fur.

The rings round the sun
grow paler.

Hay is laid in lines to allow the sheep to feed;
they would die in the trampling
if the hay were thrown in heaps.

COCKATOOS AND SHEEP
Gouache 56×76 cms (22×30 ins)

Faint barking comes from a farmhouse beyond the ridge.
A leaf-web settles on the dingo's snout.
He tilts his head for a final confirmation,
then he stands and begins to trot,
and every sense of frame and brain
meets in a judgement of his movements.
The slender body lifts and falls
as the paws feel out the ground,
guiding, steering,
with lessening time for finding the patches of sand
that make no noise,
and the quickening,
pacing action of the legs arrows
the slim shape onto open ground.

Uneasiness scuds across the sheep
as the lean intentness races onto them.
They move awkwardly on stick-like legs.
The dingo breaks them into frantic eddyings.
A sheep presents itself,
and is shielded in the wild staggering.
In the space of seconds
and a single action
the dingo slows,
turns,
picks his target and bolts through the air,
jaws open,
head held sideways,
and the wide-spaced incisors close on the sheep's throat.

A thrust of haunches and locking of jaws,
and the jagged molars burst past
wool and hide and fat
to muscle and meat.
A flick of shoulders wrenches out a tangle of flesh and arteries.
The other sheep move well away to watch;
their bleating softens.
A haunch is torn apart.
The dingo chooses his food.

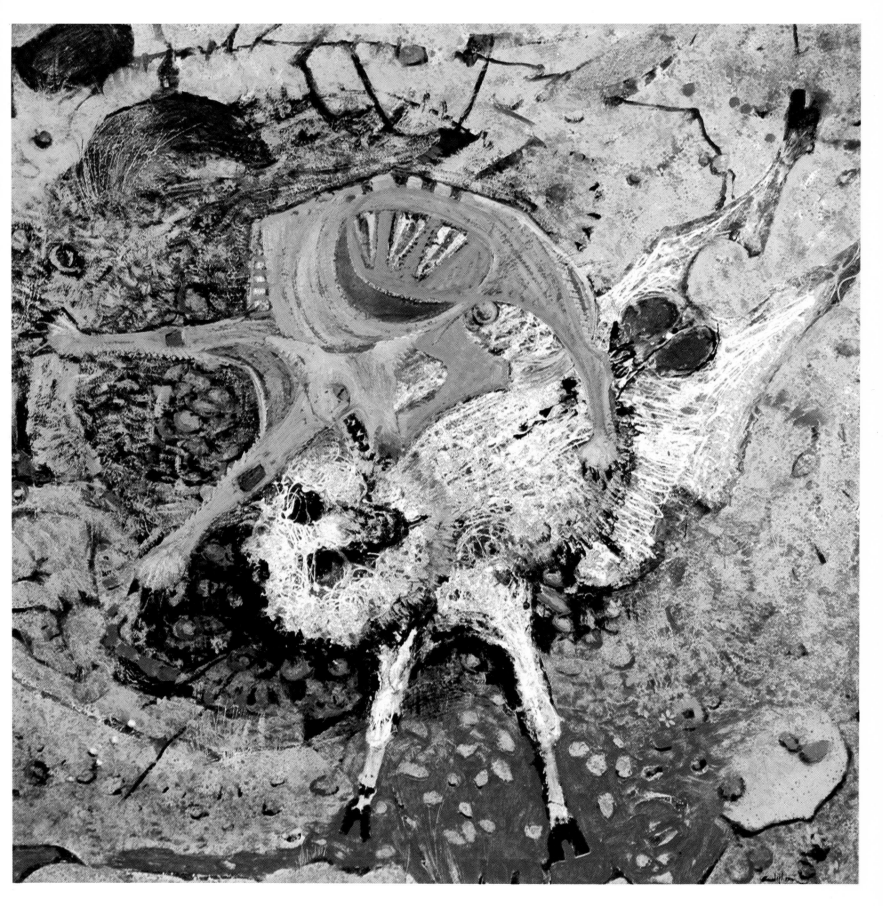

PULLING DOWN OF THE SHEEP
Oil on Hardboard 137 × 137 cms (54 × 54 ins)

The cub has been shunted to a patch of
succulent partly in shade.
The leaves are browned and acid to taste,
but there are good ones left.
The wombat has been searching them out
and saving them up.
He can still live
from the moisture left in grasses,
but grass swells the shrinking stomach
of a young cub.
It gnaws to a succulent's centre,
and its eyes reflect relief.
The wombat decides that this afternoon
he will start on a much better burrow.

Over the river,
across the valley,
and up again on far,
high ground,
the dingo adds the haunch-meat
to a store that is buried for safety
a distance from his den.
When the dingo has gone each day,
the bitch fetches meat from the cache for herself and the pups.
An unmated dingo had helped with this for a time,
but a few weeks ago he found a bitch of his own.

At the store of food the dingo trots,
wheels round and trots,
wheels round with ears high-pointed and trots,
with the lighter-coloured ruff distending
and the trotting bringing his senses to their finest tension,
wheels round and trots again.
He normally trots before moving into danger,
but this is a trotting before he moves towards peace;
he must thoroughly question his longing to visit the den,
and be certain to keep it concealed.
Four minutes of wheel and trot make up his mind,
and he moves on over a hill.

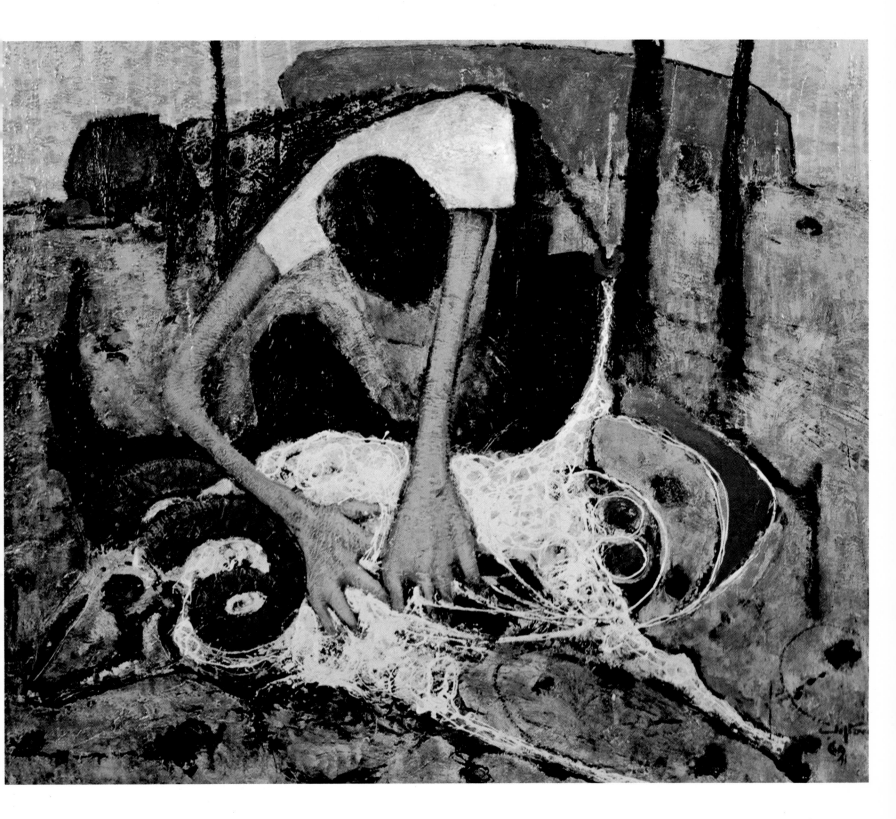

COLLECTING THE DEAD WOOL
Oil on Hardboard 91 × 110 cms (36 × 42 ins)

A lowering volume of body-water
leads to a lowering volume of blood,
and to less oxygen for animals' limbs and heads.
Livers whiten and vision fades.

The two hundred kangaroos bound south.
Three of the females leap aside
and jettison their joeys.
The joeys are the last left alive,
and a scrubland death will come sooner
than a coma in the pouch.
And joeys will grow later from embryos
in the pregnant females of the herd.
Arrested gestation when days are wrong
is the kangaroo's hope of keeping the future open.

Guns thud.
The leaders slow to a lope.
A buzzing in the sky rasps and recedes.
Dogs yelp in fury.
The kangaroos decide against the south.

SHOOTING OF THE KANGAROOS
Oil on Hardboard 91 × 122 cms (36 × 48 ins)

The dingo-bitch sits exhausted.
At the end of an hour of play
she is a flinching mound of fur,
protecting tail and ears and all four paws.
The unmated dingo used to help with games.
A quick charge from the approaching dingo
rolls both pups over and down a slope.
There is an immediate greeting,
which happens at every meeting,
even after separation was short.
Fore-legs climb on shoulders,
tongues lick at eyes and muzzles,
and the dingoes rear and dance in clumsy circles.
They brush ruffs as the pups come galloping back.
The bitch moves to the den
and the father plays.
Pup-play is a matter of trial and test,
leading to sore paws and itching tails.
The pups dart through and among the rocks and scrub
till the father's teeth have nipped a rump,
then the father's rump is the target in a lolloping,
serving chase with menacing yips.
The lesson snaps shut and the three of them blend
with earth.

A roar pours from the sky.
It swells, a shadow flicks across them,
and it goes.

For two whole hours
the wombat has worked at a burrow
— closer to tougher grass,
close to roots of a giant gum
that might provide strengthening sap.
He is slow,
so there must be no ceasing
of the gnawing of roots
and the finding of stones to force the shaft down deeper.
The burrowing reveals death to him
in the form of the hind-paws of the cub's choked mother.
The wombat's rump thrusts upward
and backward past the stones
and the chewed-off roots,
and he staggers into sunlight.
There has to be richer water.
He rubs against leaves to free his face of dust.
There is a chance at the river;
there is no chance anywhere else.
He quells his instincts and his fear
— he must take the cub to the river.

The wet mass of air is forced down
over the coastal ranges.
Ants make holes through an earthworm's skin
and begin to carry its flesh.

At sea it begins to rain.

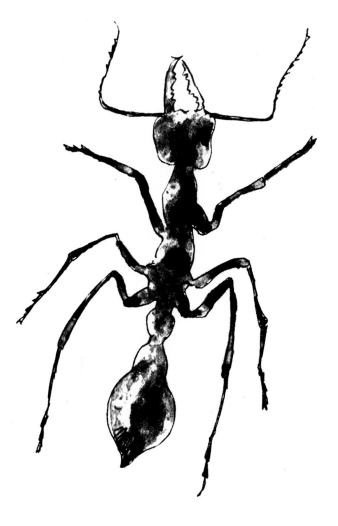

RAIN
Gouache 51 × 64 cms (20 × 25 ins)

The plane has gone and the pups have fled to the den.
There is a distant baying.
The dingo curls on his side in the shade and naps
in the manner of wolves and foxes.
Thirty seconds asleep and ten awake.
The heart-rate, thirty beats a minute.
Thirty seconds asleep and ten awake.
The tongue shoves shallow patterns in the sand.
He feels the knowledge that he must attack
the sheep again at moonrise.
The heart slackens and the breathing stills,
and a sense of Asian Pale-foot sires
forms in the eight-year-old mind.

There is loneliness and wandering and bare,
grim battle in the mist of the past.
Drought, fire, hunger, flood,
the deep searching for power in the thin,
hard sinews
— all this has gone on always,
but sometimes the dingo has met and merged with all of life,
and has welcomed beyond all further achievement
the blinding times of mating.
His bitch has thrown pups,
confirming his courage and ruthlessness.
The napping is ended by louder baying.
His bitch is standing near him.
He goes to her,
and they whistle and whine.
They rear and slide their fore-legs over each other's shoulders.
They snuffle and part.

The kangaroos surrender
to the smell of man's water-trap.
The crashing paws send up thin columns of dust
as they thunder to the north.
Three of the older males lose ground
to do whatever can be done
to delay the dangers of guns and dogs.

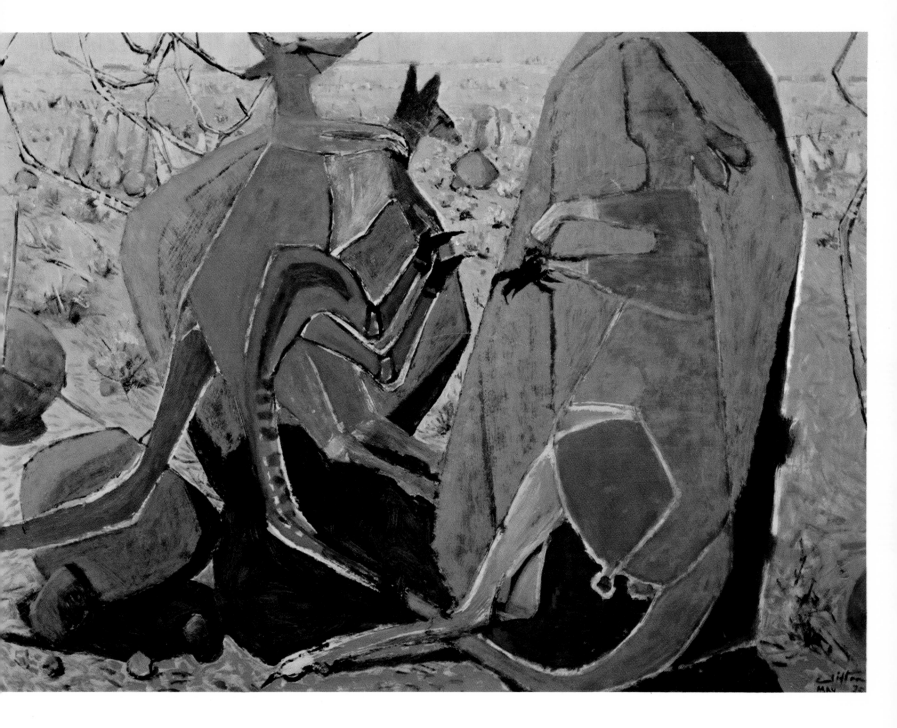

THE END RUN
Oil on Hardboard 91 × 122 cms (36 × 48 ins)

The dingo slides to a lower point of the further river.
Discovery is less likely here,
but he must confront a barbed and dense-wired fence.

The wombat stops
— to eat grass,
not to rest
— paws bracketing his snout.
There is a pain of dryness in his stomach.
He wants to doze,
but the rump lifts,
and he looks at the dead cockatoo underneath him.
Slowly he surges on again,
and the tumbling cub is propelled toward the river.

Fences that block rabbits and dingoes
cost thousands of dollars a kilometre.
Where wombats have been there are tunnels underneath,
used by dozens of dingoes and thousands of rabbits.
And so there was shooting of wombats.
But dingoes can jump;
and so hundreds of kilometres of fencing
were lifted one metre higher.
The dingo finds a lower point of the fence.
He is not quite squat on his haunches.
The hind-legs shake,
then vibrate,
and the dingo springs.
Front and back pads ripple the top strand of wire,
and he lands with a sound
that only a hare would hear.
He spots the place to save him time if he returns.

The rain at sea moves wet air
to the land and to the ranges.
The air is lifted by the swirling inland heat.
A wasp's legs harden to a twig,
where it will stay as a hollow husk
until a rush of wind or a drop of rain explodes it.
A fragment of cracked clay
falls from the nest it has left.
On the earth's rim sunlight refracts through hovering dust
to show drought's evening purple.
The early moon is pearled.

Kangaroos defer to the greyhound lines of wolves,
and they back into fights
they must sometimes have with mastiffs.
The rearguard kangaroo props
on his tail to pivot the slashing arcs of huge hind-legs.
The mastiff makes what use he can of turns and speed and surprise.
The reward for a kangaroo is time to escape from man;
the reward for a station-dog is man-carved kangaroo-meat;
this time neither lives.

Sheep are forgotten.

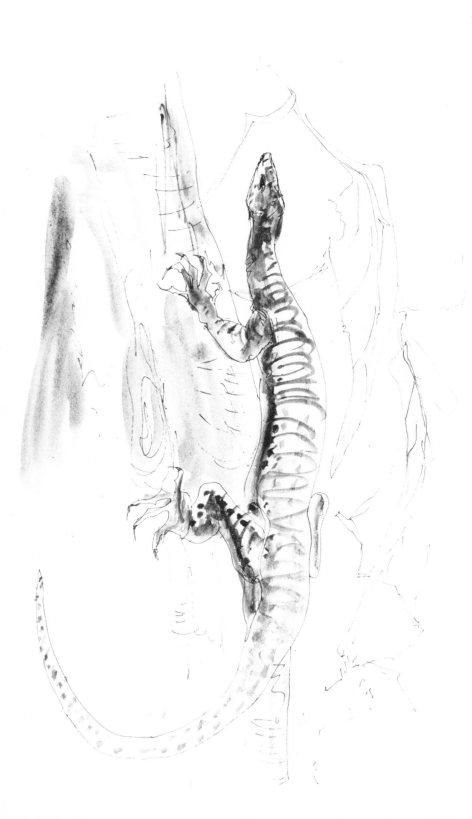

SHOOTING OF THE WILD DOGS
Oil on Hardboard 114 × 152 cms (45 × 60 ins)

The dingo's pupils pin-point
in the haze of searchlights.
It is cooler,
and the ducts are open in the hump of his snout.
The air breathed out is warmed to clear
the tissues of fore-brain and eyes.
A thread of tangled baying is spun closer.
The dingo lifts and flings
at the flank of the station-dog.
The mastiff is dazed by the ambush,
and slews and slides.
His head shakes with his snarling as the dingo leaps again.
The mastiff's jaws are snapping
but the dingo's mouth is shut.
The dog crashes at the dingo's side,
slipping on sand as the dingo wheels away,
summoning the dog to lunge again.
Lights sweep over them as the mastiff charges
at the smaller shape;
but his vision is not lit with the cunning
and endurance of the Asian Pale-foot.

The dingo taunts and tires the dog,
and his brain stays clear as the dog's eyes blur.
There are gun-shots
and sharp whistles and a ricochet's scream.
The dingo drops below a charge,
not turning aside,
rolls on his back,
and his head snaps up to clamp an upper fore-leg.
None of the dog's scrabbling
allows him more than skin-bites.
The dingo's teeth tighten,
then flash to the dog's throat.
The yelping breaks into high-pitched squealing,
and the dingo squirms from under
the convulsing weight.

He is spun off his feet by a bullet
that rifles through bones at the base of his tail.
More dogs come close.
There is a moment of indecision
as the dingo flops on his chest to slow his heart.
Sheep are forgotten,
but not the pups,
or the drought,
or his mate.
He does something that he has not done before.
He jerks meat from the mastiff's shivering body
before he races across the hill
to the point of the fence that he marked.
The head tilts to balance the meat,
the hind-legs knot and quiver,
and a searchlight traces a trembling wire
as the dingo drops below.

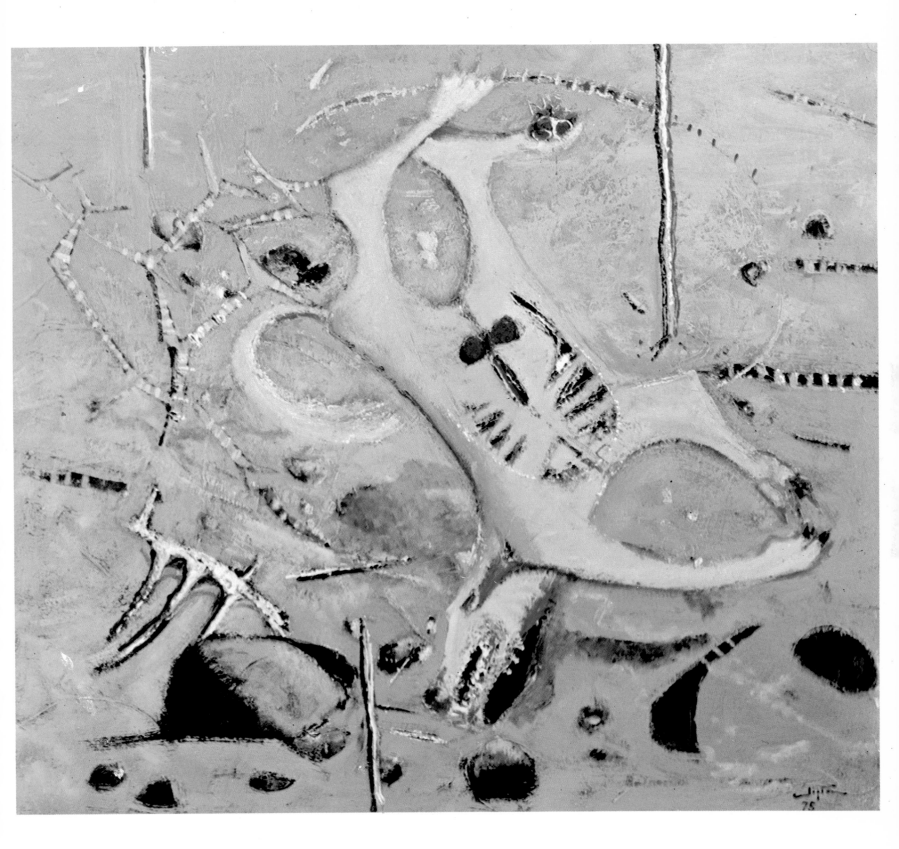

DOG DESTRUCTION
Oil on Hardboard 91 × 102 cms (36 × 40 ins)

A thundering comes closer,
not from above and not from a distance,
but shaking the earth and making pebbles jump.
Kangaroo-legs flash from the sky.
All the wombat can do is to crouch.
A paw slams his back,
and another flips his cub into the air.
The wombat waits,
then starts to look for his cub.

The tree is ten times the age of the dingo;
it is twenty times the age of the wombat.
Saplings curve with drought,
but the tree's thick bark nurses the cellulose.
Its foliage shrivels,
but there are light green buds,
and the roots reach lower than earthworms.
The sap is slowed,
not stopped.
The tree will live through this drought and the next.
Shafts of moonlight through its branches
turn a grey kookaburra silver
and a brown snake grey.

The dingo has crossed one fork of the river:
a searchlight finds him between the streams.
Shouting spurs the noise of dogs and engines,
and the ground puffs with bullets.
Fire spears his shoulder
and he drops his meat in shock.
He stands to find the meat again,
canters to the second river-fork, and swims.
There are more shots,
but the head alone is a difficult target.
Dogs strive in the water behind him,
but even a wounded dingo is faster in water as well as on land.
He comes to ground with a precious minute to roll in sand
to staunch the loss of blood.

The noses of two crouched forms are slightly apart.
The wombat blinks at the eyes of a shattered rabbit.
He tries to remember when there was anything like this before.
It must be to do with the dryness.
Something is wrong.
He edges his cub around the staring shape.
There are greater dangers than those he knows at the river,
and strength is left only for one decision.
And he thinks that water will wash off the blood
where the kangaroo-paw sliced.

An Alsatian-dog appears in front of the dingo,
unscented and undetected.
It has come from another farm,
and the chance of a clear escape has gone.
The dingo must fight again — turning, twisting,
sliding to drain the enemy's power,
thinking, probing, waiting for the chance
to dive underneath as the Alsatian's judgement fades.
Guns thud.
Dogs scramble from the river.
There is small space and no time left,
and the Alsatian's teeth rip a fragment of ear.

Shots and baying funnel the kangaroos through a narrow ravine,
and the thick smell of water leads them to cannon together.
High-wired fencing funnels them further,
and they force through a gap to a paddock
where shallow tanks of water are ringed
with a fence of strut-wired steel.
A fury of bodies pounds,
and the frenzy of drinking and wanting to drink
shuts out the sound of a plane,
and its chatter of guns machined
to be certain death.

THE SURVIVORS
Oil on Canvas 130×182 cms (51×72 ins)

Hardened stalks of grass starve bacteria,
and, later, seed-pods will ripen.
The moon begins to sink.
It rains over the sea.

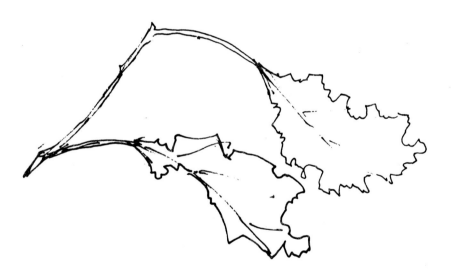

Lights and guns flash.
The Alsatian attacks again.
The dingo dives,
but is torn away by a bullet that snaps his lower ribs.
One lung starts to fill.
The Alsatian mounts above him
and the dingo bunches his paws,
but a bullet destroys the Alsatian's brain.

THE TERRITORIAL IMPERATIVE
Oil on Hardboard 91 × 122 cms (36 × 48 ins)

The dingo chooses a path that he knows well,
and his paws work hard to keep him
ahead of the mastiffs.
His body has known a fleetness
of sixty-five kilometres an hour,
but now his lungs burn
to keep him faster than thirty.
A mate, and pups, a failing of senses,
three bullets through his body —
and an immense spending of his deep energy.

The wombat listens to snarls and howls.
There is a persistent scent of death and decaying leaves.
Nothing is right.
He pushes his snout into water,
and sneezes and chokes.
He turns to his cub
and spades it into the river.
He lifts himself back,
rolls on his side,
and noise fades from his mind.
His eyes strain to focus a shape in the water.
He has done all he knows to keep the future open.

His eyelids blink to moisten the dust,
and he watches as the river adds
the dead cub to a clump of twigs.

The mastiff-flesh is buried with the store.
The dingo trots.
When Asian wolves are certain of death
they lose the instinct for concealment,
and they can sometimes be traced
when they try to return to their dens.
And many bitches and pups have been shot
when hunters let dying dingoes have their heads.
The moon streaks the dingo's fur
with amber and amethyst,
and blackens the blood in the sand.
The trotting stops.
He snuffles his paws.
He stares in the direction of his den,
then moves *away* from it
on a track that takes him to a high,
bare knoll that juts from a cliff.
His mate and the pups will live.

The kangaroos lie in a hunched mass,
in a littering of twitching necks and tails.
One by one,
three subtract themselves from the huddle,
and lope around the encircling wire.
By moonset the mass is motionless.

The sun rises in extending light-blue circles.
Wallabies and wasps and snakes and wagtails are quiet.
The land burns and the air stares.

The dingo is dead when he is found.
He is on his side,
his head slewed back,
the pale tongue laced with parading ants.
The hard, crystalled eyes look out
across the rough skin of Australia.
He has kept the future open.
Not a dog.
Not a wolf.

This is his country.
He is still king of it.

THE DEATH OF THE DINGO
Gouache 57 × 77 cms (22½ × 30½ ins)

Catalogue of Paintings